Together
We Go Places

By Jennifer Schroer

Illustrations by Tosin Akinwande

Printed in the United States of America

ISBN 978-1-7362142-2-0 (hardcover)
ISBN 978-1-7362142-0-6 (paperback)
ISBN 978-1-7362142-1-3 (ebook)

Canoe Tree Press
4697 Main Street
Manchester Center, VT 05255

Canoe Tree Press is a division of DartFrog Books.

To my mooncakes—California, Diem and Kevan.
Imagine your dream, you can do anything.

Together we go places
to get our errands done.

Each day we have a different task
all are so much fun.

Monday starts the week
with a trip to see the doctor.

My sister really hates her shots
so I go with to watch her.

I hold her hand
to help her through
and later we go to the zoo.

Tuesday is the day
for shopping
we pick out food
and corn for popping.

Mom drives to the bank for cash
then takes us out to spend our stash.

To the candy store we run
my sister picks a lollypop, I get gum.

Wednesday we go to the park
I run, I climb, I hear dogs bark.

It's so much fun, I think it's cool
my sister's almost out of school.

We pick her up with time to spare
then hit the salon to style our hair.

Thursday comes
and now it's time

to go on a walk
with friends of mine.

We meet each week to laugh and chat
when it's cold outside, I wear my hat.

Friday's here,
it's dinner time
mom gets dressed up
and sips her wine.

Dad takes us out
for fancy food

we mind our manners,
sometimes we're good.

It's mom's birthday,
time to celebrate!

We get dessert
and clean our plates.

Saturday is action-packed
gymnastics, dance,
then time for snacks.

We exercise and play for hours
then get cleaned up to smell like flowers.

We snuggle up for movie night
we sit by mom;
She holds us tight.

Sunday is the day for family
daddy, mom, my sister and me.

Next week we'll take
a family vacation

we plan to drive
across the nation.

Together we go places
it brings a smile to all our faces.

ABOUT THE AUTHOR

Jennifer Schroer is a financial services industry professional and mother of two. She and her family reside in the San Francisco Bay Area, California. You can visit her online on Instagram @Together_We_Go_Places.